Beautiful Baby

a record book about you

Tiny hand that lies in mine, so steadily you trust.
I care for you and when you cry, comfort you I must.
And in exchange for all of me, you, from, your infant cup,
will teach me what it is to see what I miss being grown up.
I pray you will be good to all your fellowmen and Nature,
and that I will "grow down" while you
grow up for your adventure.

This book is dedicated to

_____

The greatest blessing
for a parent
is a child like you...

YOUR PARENTS

This is all about your mother.
Her full name is...
and she was born...

These are some of the things that make her special...

Before you came, she...

Her thoughts about having you...

photo

photo

This is all about your father.
His full name is...
and he was born...

These are some of the things that make him special...

Before you came, he...

His thoughts about having you...

These are your grandparents.
Their full names are...

_____

_____

They came from...

_____

and had this to say about your coming...

_____

Here are some photographs of them...

_____

photo

photo

photo

photo

These are your aunts and uncles, both those by family ties and those by choice...

_____

_____

What their expectations were of you..._____

_____

Here are some photographs of them...

Family is not
just the tree,
but the creatures
that live in it and
around it.

photo

photo

photo

Extended family who were part of your life then...

_____

_____

_____

_____

_____

Some of your mother's friends...

_____

_____

Some of your father's friends...

_____

_____

photo

We all make of Earth a home together.

SPECIAL MOMENTS BEFORE YOU CAME

What we felt when we found out you were coming...

_____

_____

_____

What it was like to be pregnant with you...

_____

_____

_____

Just being quiet with you inside...

_____

_____

_____

Thoughts and dreams we had during our wait...

_____

_____

_____

Magic, mystery, marvel
our little wonder
in the making...

BABY SHOWER

photo/invitation

space

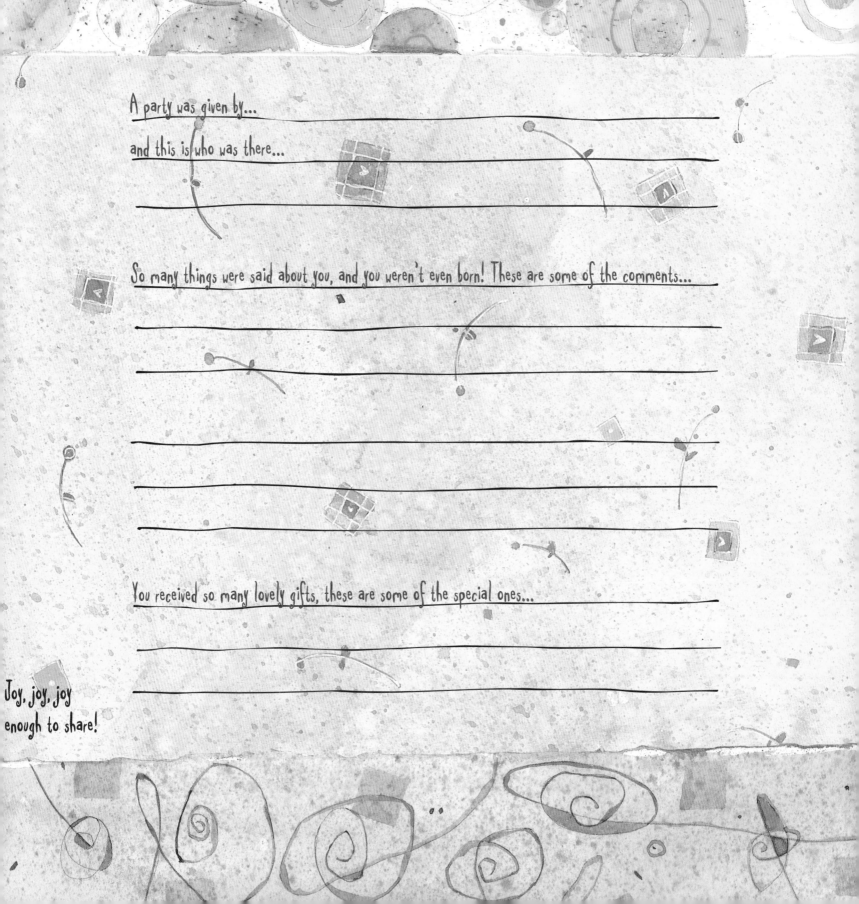

A party was given by...

and this is who was there...

So many things were said about you, and you weren't even born! These are some of the comments...

You received so many lovely gifts, these are some of the special ones...

Joy, joy, joy
enough to share!

SOME SPECIAL MEMORIES
AS WE GOT READY FOR YOU...

These are some of the things we did just because you were coming...

_____

_____

_____

I remember some of our hopes (and fears)...

_____

_____

_____

What we planned for your future...

_____

_____

_____

We got lots of advice. The best advice we got, though, was from...

_____

and they said...

_____

_____

faith in what's to come,
hope in its goodness...

We generally agreed on what your surroundings should be. How we wanted it to be...

_____

_____

And then, we had to compromise...

_____

_____

_____

_____

_____

_____

A happy place
is one filled with love.

photo

AND THEN
YOU CAME

photo

This is the story of your birth...

_____

_____

Your eyes were... _____

and your hair was... _____

You arrived on... _____ at... _____

You were delivered by... _____ at... _____

Your weight and measurements were... _____

You were named... _____

because of... _____

Nothing can prepare one for
the joy and awe of parenthood...

SOME OF THE PEOPLE WHO CAME TO GREET YOU

This is who came...

_____

_____

_____

and this is what they had to say about you...

_____

_____

Special messages for you...

_____

_____

_____

_____

_____

photo

COMING HOME

We made big changes. Some of the changes in our home because of you...

This is your first photograph, taken...

photo

No words wide enough
tall enough, large enough
to describe my feelings
for you...

photo/announcement space

This is how we announced and celebrated your coming...

It takes more than
roots —
water, air, love and care.

YOUR FAMILY TREE

_____

grandfather   grandmother

_____

father

_____

you

_____

mother

_____

grandfather   grandmother

FOR SAFEKEEPING, YOUR BIRTH CERTIFICATE

Certificate space

raISed In Good FAIth

We had a special event to receive you into our midst. This is what we did...

_____

_____

Who we figure will be your angels...

_____

_____

Special messages from special people...

_____

_____

_____

_____

Looking at you,
your hands, your toes,
your little eyes, only
God could make one
like you.

YOUR FIRST BATH

And what a splash that was! It was given by...

_____

_____

_____

This is what it was like...

_____

_____

_____

and your reaction to it was...

_____

_____

_____

_____

The two best friends
of little children,
water and dirt!

photo

And here you are...

THE FIRSTS

First time you smiled...

The first night you slept through...

You sat up when you were...

Started crawling at...

Your first solid food...

First tooth...

Kisses and waves...

You clapped your hands...

MORE FIRSTS

First words...

_____

_____

_____

Pulled yourself up and walked hanging on...

_____

First steps alone...

_____

Started talking in earnest...

_____

THEN THERE'S THE FIRST HAIRCUT

It was on... given by... and your reaction to it was...

_____

_____

_____

A funny thing that happened that day was...

_____

_____

photo/lock of hair space

Sleeping and Eating

What we remember the most about feeding you...

_____

_____

What you liked to eat...

_____

Special treats you liked to gum away at...

_____

And then there was sleeping...

Your favorite places...

Some strange positions...

_____

Those special sleeping partners you loved...

_____

_____

May you feel safe
in your slumber...

EARLY TIMES WITH YOUR FATHER

This is what you two used to do...
_____

_____

Where you liked to go together...
_____

_____

Some traits you got from him...
_____

_____

_____

His favorite things about you...
_____

_____

_____

As a child, he feels he was like you in...
_____

_____

_____

nothing like Dad and his baby...

photo

EARLY TIMES WITH YOUR MOTHER

This is what you two used to do....

_____

_____

Where you liked to go together...

_____

Some traits you got from her...

_____

_____

_____

Her favorite things about you are...

_____

_____

_____

As a child, she feels she was like you in...

_____

_____

During the best of times,
during the worst of times,
mothers are a solace to all.

photo

SOME OF YOUR FAVORITE THINGS

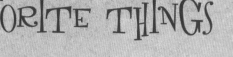

You were so happy, and many things made you happy. Here are some of your favorites.

_____

Your favorite game... _____

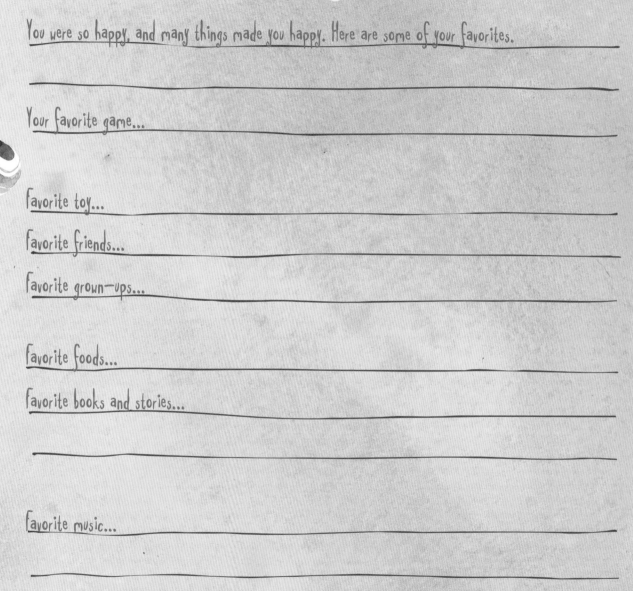

favorite toy... _____

favorite friends... _____

favorite grown-ups... _____

favorite foods... _____

favorite books and stories... _____

_____

favorite music... _____

_____

photo

SOME THINGS YOU JUST DIDN'T LIKE

Some foods you didn't like...

_____

_____

_____

Sights and sounds that made you cry...

_____

_____

_____

Your least favorite activity...

_____

_____

_____

You sure let us know
how you feel about things!

CATCHING YOU IN THE ACT!

Little mischief we caught you doing...

_____

_____

_____

_____

Cute things you did...

_____

_____

_____

_____

_____

_____

You little rascal!

CASUAL, ELEGANT: WHAT YOU WORE

We remember your favorite clothes were...

_____

And what you would hang out in...

_____

And some of your most elegant threads were...

_____

Then there was that which you would not wear...

_____

Whatever you wear,
it doesn't change
your loveliness inside...

Start experiencing
the world
and make it
better.

YOUR FIRST DOCUMENTED TRIP

This is where we went...

_____

Some special memories about that trip...

_____

_____

Your first impressions about travel...

_____

_____

As a traveler you were...

_____

_____

photo

SPECIAL FAMILY CELEBRATIONS DURING YOUR FIRST YEAR OF LIFE

Other births during that time...

_____

_____

_____

family reunions you attended...

_____

_____

_____

What people said about you...

_____

_____

_____

Weddings you got to go to...

_____

_____

_____

Sharing the joy...

photo

HAPPY BIRTHDAY!

Finally you are 1! We celebrated by...

_____

_____

_____

_____

_____

_____

Those who celebrated with you...

_____

_____

How you felt about being 1...

_____

Something special you did that day...

_____

A special gift you got was...

given to you by...

May every year
bring you
more and more
blessings and love.

photo

LOOKING FORWARD TO NEXT YEAR

Plans we made for your second year...

_____

_____

_____

_____

_____

If we could ask anything about your future, we would want to know...

_____

_____

Your character is showing. We know that you will be...

_____

_____

Can't wait to see
how you will turn out!